THE LITTLE MERMAID
WHO COULD NOT SING

THE LITTLE MERMAID

WHO COULD NOT SING

LOUIS SLOBODKIN

THE MACMILLAN COMPANY

NEW YORK

First Printing

PRINTED IN THE UNITED STATES OF AMERICA

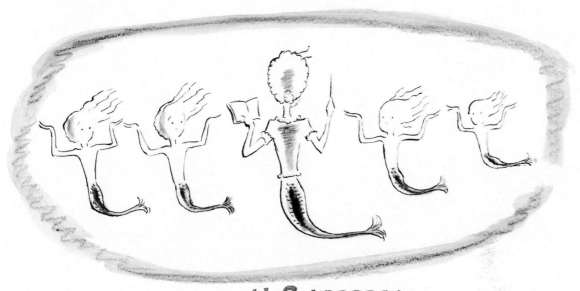

U. S. 1028801

THE LITTLE MERMAID
WHO COULD NOT SING

A long time ago, when mermaids splashed gaily about in the glittering distant seas, there were schools of little mermaids, the same as there are schools of fishes. And it was at these schools that the little mermaids learned all the things they ought to know before they grew up.

They learned such things as Swimming Gracefully, Dancing O'er the Waves and Riding Sea Horses. And, too, there were classes in Arts and Seacrafts.

5

(Weaving seaweed doilies and making necklaces of colored shells were some of the seacrafts.) And most important of all was a class where they were taught Singing on the Rocks. Because as everyone knows, "singing on the rocks as they comb their beautiful hair" is what mermaids do most of the time.

One of the best schools of mermaids was the Blue Rocks School which was somewhere out in the center of the great Southern Sea. There were good teachers for all the classes but the teacher who taught singing in that school was the best of all.

Now everyone believes that all little mermaids always had long golden hair and that they all sang wonderfully sweet. But that is not exactly true!

There was once a little mermaid who had long bright red hair. And she could not sing wonderfully sweet . . . and she knew it! Her name was Cynthia and she had come to the Blue Rocks School from a distant Northern sea.

On her first day at school Cynthia got along very nicely in almost all of the classes. She swam gracefully and delighted the dancing teacher with the way she danced through the waves. She rode her sea horse as swiftly as any of the others and was better than many of them in Arts and Seacrafts.

But when she came to the singing class she did not do so well . . . not at all!

All the little mermaids gathered on the Blue Rocks at the end of the day for the singing class. The singing teacher sat on the highest rock. She began the class by saying:

"Now Girls . . . First we shall sing our school song, 'Hail to Thee, Fair Blue Rocks' . . . I shall sing it first . . . alone."

She blew her seashell pitch pipe once and sang:

> *"Oh . . . To be where the Blue Rocks*
> *Rise out of the Sea . . . of the Sea*
> *There our hearts turn ever*
> *Ever longingly . . . longingly.*
> *So Hail to Thee, Fair Blue Rocks*
> *Hail oh joyously . . . joyously.*
> *We shall ne'er forget thee, Blue Rocks*
> *Where ever we may be . . . we may be."*

"Now," said the singing teacher, "everyone get out combs and we'll sing together. Comb and sing . . . sing and comb . . . One, two . . . one, two . . . begin."

And the little mermaids combed their hair to the rhythm of the song and they all sang beautifully . . . all except one!

That one was Cynthia. Although she loved to sing, she knew she could not, and she sat quietly on one of the lower rocks hoping that the singing teacher could not see her in the fading light.

But the singing teacher had very sharp eyes and she soon saw that Cynthia was not singing. She raised her hands and stopped the class.

"You are not all singing," she said with a sweet voice. And she was looking right at Cynthia! "You must sing. That is why you came to school. Now let us begin again. Everyone sing . . . One, two . . . One, two . . . begin!"

Little Cynthia sang as softly as she could, hoping that the great chorus of little mermaids and the sound of the waves breaking up against the rocks would drown out her voice. But try as she might her voice was heard above all the others!

It was a deep screech-owl of a voice or something like a tremendous bullfrog . . . or perhaps it was more like a hoarse gigantic foghorn!

The singing teacher waved her arms wildly!

"Stop! . . . Please stop!" she cried. Then she took a long breath and she looked at Cynthia again.

This time she smiled gently and put one finger to her tightly closed lips.

Cynthia understood what the singing teacher meant. She was telling Cynthia that it was all right if Cynthia did not sing with the class.

The teacher led them through a great favorite "Comb and sing . . . Sing and comb . . . As we skip . . . O'er the ocean's foam" . . . and other popular mermaid songs. But before each song she took the precaution to smile gently at Cynthia and touch one finger to her tightly closed lips.

When the singing class was over and all the other little mermaids had dashed off for one last swim before supper the singing teacher gave Cynthia a private singing lesson.

Cynthia tried very hard to sing wonderfully sweet, but with little . . . really no . . . success.

At last the singing teacher took her hands off her ears (where she had kept them through most of that lesson) and sighed.

"Well," she said, "at least you do try, Cynthia. Now we will have another private lesson tomorrow. Meanwhile you need not sing with the others during class . . . I am sure I can help your voice . . .

It is still a little . . . I think you might make a good strong bass if you work at it . . . Now off you go for your swim."

And after little Cynthia with a flip of her tail dashed into the sea the singing teacher sat there wondering how she could fit a deep bass voice into a chorus of little mermaids.

From then on and for a long time (so it seemed to her) Cynthia had private lessons from the music teacher. But she always had to sit silently on her rock during the regular singing classes.

Cynthia's lessons were just voice exercises and scales . . . and scales and voice exercises . . . over and over and over again. She was not permitted to sing one song! And she did so want to sing some of the beautiful songs that the other little mermaids sang.

And she might have gone on singing scales and doing voice exercises for . . . no one knows how long . . . because her voice really did not improve much, if something unforeseen had not happened.

A big sailing ship had been blown off her course and had drifted into the great uncharted Southern Sea. No mortal man had ever sailed those waters before. And no mortal man-made maps showed any of the sandbars and rocks that were spotted throughout that great body of water.

The wind died down as it usually does after a great storm. And for days the sailors were uneasy as they waited for the wind to rise again and fill the ship's sails. At last the Captain ordered the sailors to pull up some of the deck timbers and carve them into great oars. He planned to have the ship rowed out of the great Southern Sea and back again to more familiar waters.

The Captain stood up on the prow of the ship on the lookout for any rocks or sandbars that might wreck his ship. He would shout, "Pull Starboard" when he wanted his sailors to pull stronger on the oars on the right side of the ship. And he shouted, "Pull Larboard" when he wanted them to pull stronger on the left ones.

And it was just as the sun was setting at the end of a very hot day and as the big ship was being rowed across the center of the great Southern Sea, when a golden mist came up that shrouded everything within sight. But the Captain kept his ship moving; he called up two sharp-eyed sailors to stand lookout with him and he kept the rest of the crew at the oars.

At the Blue Rocks School of Mermaids the regular Singing on the Rocks class had just begun. It seemed to the singing teacher as she sat on the topmost rock in that golden mist, that the little mermaids were at their very best that evening.

Their voices floated out across the waters of the great Southern Sea sweet and clear. Their singing sounded like distant silvery bells and the whispering of soft breezes through sea-foam.

The Captain heard the beautful sound of the singing mermaids but he had no idea what it was. It seemed to beckon to him and he could not resist the exquisite sound. In a low voice he ordered his men to "Pull Starboard" and to "Pull Larboard" until he had steered his ship directly toward the mist-hidden Blue Rocks!

Little Cynthia sat silently, as usual, on her rock down near the lapping waves. She swayed gently to and fro with the beautiful music. And she felt, if she did not sing out with the others, she would just . . . just . . . burst!

And at last when the singing teacher called on the class to sing the school song once more . . . Cynthia could hold back no longer!

She burst forth and sang at the top of her lungs!

"O-O-OH . . . TO . . . BE WHERE . . .
    THE BLUE ROCKS
    RISE OUT OF THE SEA . . ."

It was just at that very moment the prow of the big sailing ship pierced the golden mist that surrounded the Blue Rocks!

The Captain up on the prow got the full blast of little Cynthia's great voice! . . . her great screech-owl-bullfrog-gigantic-foghorn of a voice!

"BACKWATER!" he shouted, "BACKWATER FOR YOUR LIVES!"

In the nick of time he had seen the Blue Rocks
rising out of the sea!

The men almost broke their oars . . . so hard
did they pull to save their ship and keep it from
crashing up on the rocks.

"A MONSTER! . . . A MONSTER!" screamed the little mermaids.

They had just caught one frightening glimpse of the ship with the men standing on her prow before she was pulled away. They had never seen any ships or people before.

In a few minutes the danger was over. The sailors

had rowed the ship safely away from the Blue Rocks
and they kept right on rowing as fast as they could
go. And the little mermaids recovered from their
fright. Most of them believed they had seen a monster which surely would have crushed them all, had
it not been for Cynthia.

After the sailing ship was a safe distance away from the Blue Rocks, the Captain turned to the two sailors who stood lookout with him.

"That was a mighty close call," he said. "Who sounded that foghorn? . . . Who shouted BEWARE?"

The sailors shook their heads. The younger sailor had a strange glassy look in his eyes.

"Captain," he said in a hushed voice, "did you see them, Captain?"

"See who?" asked the Captain coldly.

"The little mermaids!" said the sailor. "Dozens of them! . . . Beautiful little mermaids as I live and breathe!"

"Bosh!" growled the Captain. "There's no such things as mermaids! . . . You had better get back to the oars."

And on the Blue Rocks the little mermaids chattered excitedly together. The youngest mermaids were sure it had been a Monster they saw. But some of the older ones insisted it was a ship with people on it. They had heard of ships and people though none of them had ever seen any.

"Nonsense!" said the singing teacher impatiently. "There are no such things as ships and people!"

But even though the Captain had said there were
no such things as mermaids, whenever he heard a
beautiful sound like distant silvery bells and the
whisper of a soft breeze through sea-foam, coming
across the waters . . . he quickly brought his ship
about . . . and sailed in the opposite direction as
fast as he could go.

And although the singing teacher had said there were no such things as ships and people, whenever a fog or mist came up around the Blue Rocks during the singing class, she would promptly call on little Cynthia to sing the school song . . . as a solo!

And happy little Cynthia would lift her great voice and blast out joyously to her heart's content:

"O-O-OH . . . TO . . . BE WHERE . . .
THE BLUE ROCKS
RISE OUT OF THE SEA. . . ."

THE
END